Reading

REVISION

Laura Collinson

RISING STARS

Acknowledgements

Rising Stars is grateful to the following schools who will be utilising Achieve to prepare their students for the National Tests: Chacewater Community Primary School, Cornwall; Coppice Primary School, Essex; Edgewood Primary School, Notts; Henwick Primary School, Eltham; Norwood Primary School, Southport; Sacred Heart Catholic Primary School, Manchester; Sunnyfields Primary School, Hendon; Tennyson Road Primary School, Luton.

Photo credits

Photos from iStock: p9 bus © RTimages; p13 clock © mladn61; p15 snow shovel © wwing; p19 candle © RTimages; p21 chocolate © sumnersgraphicsinc; p23 fossil © Fyletto; p24 car © schlol; p25 watch © Gary Alvis; p27 goat © Antagain; pp29, 40 © dragon Sylphe_7; p31 gingerbread house © RuthBlack; p33 acorn © tomashkop; p35 horse © Lorado; p37 flames © DrPAS; p39 stack of books © skodonnell; p41 heart © Grotmarsel; p43 witch on broomstick © shelma1; p44 gift © dejan750; p45 snake © futureimage; p49 black cat © GlobalP; p51 plums © Anna Kucherova; p53 puppies © Alona Rjabceva; p54 dinosaur © Syldavia; p55 butterfly © fototdietrich; p57 toothpaste © mphillips007

Text extracts

p8 Chocolate teapot by Paul Harris © Daily Mail; pp9, 11 Alone on a Wide Sea, reprinted by permission of HarperCollins Publishers Ltd © 2006 Michael Morpurgo; p10 Bishopsteignton Outdoor Art Group; pp11, 22 Reproduced from Usborne Science Encyclopaedia by permission of Usborne Publishing, 83-85 Saffron Hill, London EC1N 8RT, UK.www.usborne.com. Copyright © 2009 Usborne Publishing Ltd; pp11, 20, 36 Extract from Beowulf and the Monster Copyright © 1999 Brian Patten, published by permission of Barrington Stoke Ltd; p12 From What Mr Darwin Saw by Mick Manning and Brita Granstrom, published by Frances Lincoln Ltd, copyright © 2009; p13, 50 The Witch's Tears, reprinted by permission of HarperCollins Publishers Ltd © 1996 written by Jenny Nimmo; 'Keeping your child quiet with a computer could WRECK their eyesight' by Helen Carroll © Daily Mail; p14 Article from Tiggywinkles, Wildlife Hospital Trust, Registered Charity Number 286447; p15 Polar Survival Handbook, copyright © Miles Kelly Publishing Ltd 2012; Climate Change and Global Warming © Dr Kerry Kriger, www.savethefrogs.com; p18 Approximately 75 words from Percy Jackson and the Last Olympian by Rick Riordan (Puffin, 2010). Copyright © Rick Riordan, 2009; p19 A Spell to Cure Sorrow and Create Joy by Clare Bevan; The Magician's Nephew by C.S. Lewis copyright © C.S. Lewis Pte. Ltd. 1955. Extracts reprinted by permission; p21 Roald Dahl article taken from First News; p23 Five Tales from Shakespeare by Meg Harris Williams, published by Clunie Press 1996 www.artlit.info; p24 Reproduced from The Story of Cars by permission of Usborne Publishing, 83-85 Saffron Hill, London EC1N 8RT, UK. www.usborne.com. Copyright © 2007 Usborne Publishing Ltd; p25 Darke Academy by Gabriella Poole, published by Hodder Children's Books 2009; p26 Roller coasters extract from First News; p27 Excerpt from The Shaman's Apprentice: A Tale of the Amazon's Forest by Lynne Cherry and Mark J Plotkin. Text copyright © 1998 by Lynne Cherry and Mark J. Plotkin. Reprinted by permission of Houghton Mifflin Harcourt Publishing Company. All rights reserved; Shipwrecked! The Orchard Book of Heroes & Villains by Tony Bradman & Tony Ross, published by Orchard Books, an Hachette UK Company; pp28, 42 Treasure Island by Robert Louis Stevenson, published by Kingfisher 2005; p29 How to Train Your Dragon by Cressida Cowell, published by Little, Brown and Company & Hachette Children's Group; The Caractacus Chariot Company by Mike Johnson; p30 The Secret Diary of a Dragon by Sheila Simmons; p31 The Advertisement from This Poem Doesn't Rhyme by Cornelius Doyle; Reasons to live near a volcano www.geography-site.co.uk; p32 The Selfish Giant by Oscar Wilde; p33 'Squirrels' © Celia Warren, first published in The Works – Paul Cookson, Macmillan, 2000; p34 Did you know www.didyouknow. it; p35 Study maths and science for space jobs, urges astronaut by Anna Davis © Evening Standard; Farm Boy, reprinted by permission of HarperCollins Publishers Ltd © 2011 Michael Morpurgo; p37 'Matilda who told lies' from Cautionary Tales by Hilaire Belloc, reprinted by permission of Peters Fraser & Dunlop (www.petersfraserdunlop. com) on behalf of the Estate of Hilaire Belloc; p39 School day © EreadingWorksheets.com; p40 Hiccup interview taken from First News; p41 Flooding © EreadingWorksheets.com; p43 Macbeth by William Shakespeare; p44 Approximately 200 words from The Diary of a Young Girl: The Definitive Edition by Anne Frank, edited by Otto H Frank and Mirjam Pressler, translated by Susan Massotty (Viking, 1997) copyright © The Anne Frank-Fonds, Basle, Switzerland, 1991. English translation copyright © Doubleday a division of Bantam Doubleday Dell Publishing Group Inc, 1995; pp46, 48 The Lion, the Witch and the Wardrobe by C.S. Lewis copyright © C.S. Lewis Pte. Ltd. 1950. Extracts reprinted by permission; p47 Rainbows from Paint a Poem by Moira Andrew; Fossils website poetry by Ogden Nash; p48 Python on Piccolo (39 lines) in I Had a Little Cat – Collected Poems for Children by Charles Causley, published by Macmillan; p49 The Night is a Big Black Cat by G. Orr Clark; Sea Shoal See Shows on the Sea Bed by Paul Cookson; pp51, 52 The Iron Man by Ted Hughes, Faber & Faber 1986; p51 A Sudden Puff of Glittering Smoke by Anne Fine, published by Egmont; p52 Matilda by Roald Dahl, published by Jonathan Cape Ltd & Penguin Books Ltd; p53 The Bright Pavilions by Hugh Walpole; p55 Fireworks © EreadingWorksheets.com; p57 The Marvellous Homework and Housework Machine by Ken Nesbitt

Every effort has been made to trace all copyright holders, but if any have been inadvertently overlooked, the Publishers will be pleased to make the necessary arrangements at the first opportunity.

Although every effort has been made to ensure that website addresses are correct at time of going to press, Rising Stars cannot be held responsible for the content of any website mentioned in this book. It is sometimes possible to find a relocated web page by typing in the address of the home page for a website in the URL window of your browser.

Hachette UK's policy is to use papers that are natural, renewable and recyclable products and made from wood grown in sustainable forests. The logging and manufacturing processes are expected to conform to the environmental regulations of the country of origin.

ISBN: 978 1 78339 545 3

© Rising Stars UK Ltd 2015

First published in 2015 by Rising Stars UK Ltd, part of Hodder Education, an Hachette UK Company

Carmelite House

50 Victoria Embankment

London EC4Y 0DZ

www.risingstars-uk.com

Author: Laura Collinson

Author (pages 18–19, 38–45): Ione Branton

Series Editor: Helen Lewis

Accessibility Reviewer: Vivien Kilburn

Publishers: Kate Jamieson and Laura White

Project Manager: Estelle Lloyd

Editorial: Sarah Davies, Rachel Evans, Anne Kilraine, Fiona Leonard

Cover design: Burville-Riley Partnership

Illustrations by John Storey

Text design and typeset by the Pen and Ink Book Company Ltd

Printed by the Gutenberg Press, Malta

A catalogue record for this title is available from the British Library.

Contents

Welcome to Achieve Key Stage 2 Reading Revision Book 100

In this book you will find all the activities and information you need to achieve the expected scaled score of 100 in the Key Stage 2 Reading test.

About the Key Stage 2 Reading National Test

The test will take place in the summer term in Year 6. It will be done in your school and will be marked by examiners – not by your teacher.

In the test you will be given a booklet containing a range of texts and another booklet for your answers. The texts will be from a range of fiction, non-fiction and poetry. The first text will be the easiest and the last text will be the most challenging. The texts and questions will be very similar to the texts that you have been reading in school. You will have one hour to read the texts and complete the answer booklet.

The test is worth a total of 50 marks.

- Some questions ask you to find the answer in the text. These questions are usually worth 1 mark. These make up 44–66 % of the marks.
- Some questions ask you to write a short answer. These questions are usually worth 2 marks. They make up 20–40 % of the marks.
- Other questions ask you to write a longer answer. These are worth 3 marks. They make up 6–24 % of the marks.

Test techniques

Before the test

- Try to revise little and often, rather than in long sessions.
- Choose a time of day when you are not tired or hungry.
- Choose somewhere quiet so you can focus.
- Revise with a friend. You can encourage and learn from each other.
- Read the 'Top tips' throughout this book to remind you of important points in answering test questions.
- Use the advice given in this book when you are reading your own reading book. Ask yourself some of the questions as you read along.
- KEEP READING all kinds of non-fiction, fiction and poetry texts.

During the test

- READ THE QUESTION AND READ IT AGAIN.
- If you find a question difficult to answer, move on; you can always come back to it later.
- Always answer a multiple-choice question. If you really can't work out the answer, have a guess.
- Check to see how many marks a question is worth. Have you written enough to 'earn' those marks in your answer?
- Read the question again after you have answered it. Check you have done what the question asked you to do.
- If you have any time left at the end, go back to the questions you have missed. If you really do not know the answers, make guesses.

Where to get help

- Pages 8–57 will help you develop the skills you need to achieve a scaled score of 100 in the test.

- Page 58 contains a glossary to help you understand key terms about writing, reading and grammar.

- Pages 59–60 provide the answers to the 'Try this' questions.

How to use this book

1 ***Introduction*** – This section introduces each assessable element so you know what you need to achieve.

2 ***What you need to know*** – Important facts about the assessable elements are given in this section. Read them carefully. Words in lilac are defined in the glossary at the back of the book.

3 ***Text examples*** – These are short extracts from the types of text you can expect to find in the Key Stage 2 Reading National Test.

4 ***Let's practise*** – This gives an example question for you to read through. Follow the steps carefully and work through the example.

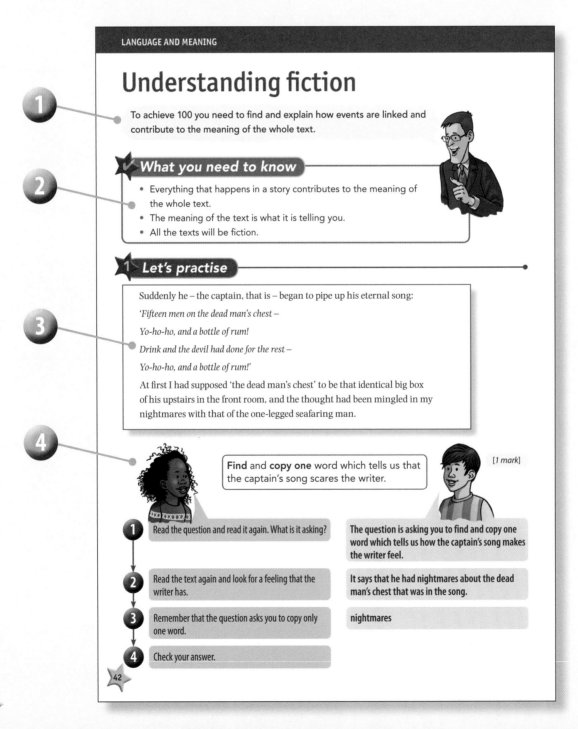

LANGUAGE AND MEANING

Understanding fiction

1 To achieve 100 you need to find and explain how events are linked and contribute to the meaning of the whole text.

What you need to know

2
* Everything that happens in a story contributes to the meaning of the whole text.
* The meaning of the text is what it is telling you.
* All the texts will be fiction.

Let's practise

3
Suddenly he – the captain, that is – began to pipe up his eternal song:

'Fifteen men on the dead man's chest –

Yo-ho-ho, and a bottle of rum!

Drink and the devil had done for the rest –

Yo-ho-ho, and a bottle of rum!'

At first I had supposed 'the dead man's chest' to be that identical big box of his upstairs in the front room, and the thought had been mingled in my nightmares with that of the one-legged seafaring man.

4

Find and copy one word which tells us that the captain's song scares the writer. [1 mark]

1 Read the question and read it again. What is it asking?

The question is asking you to find and copy one word which tells us how the captain's song makes the writer feel.

2 Read the text again and look for a feeling that the writer has.

It says that he had nightmares about the dead man's chest that was in the song.

3 Remember that the question asks you to copy only one word.

nightmares

4 Check your answer.

42

5 Try this – Practise answering the questions for yourself.

6 Glossary – A glossary for each practice test is provided to help with tricky words.

7 Top tips – These hints help you to do your best. Use them well.

LANGUAGE AND MEANING

 Try this

5

1

I had to do it. Just this once. Mr Adams was not going to hurt Ella any more.

He'd worked his way through the class. I'd been punished more than once and I knew just how it felt. As he raised his hand, I knew I had to protect my sister. I leaped onto his arm. Mr Adams stumbled against the wooden desk and fell backwards as Ella cowered in the corner.

'Leave her alone,' I cried. 'You're a bully, you know that?' I shouted, secretly quivering inside. A noise behind me told me that the rest of the class were standing up, beating their desks with their fists and cheering.

Find and **copy one** word that tells us how the writer is actually feeling during this passage. [1 mark]

_____

2

**Act 1, Scene 1. A desert place
Enter three witches.**

First witch: When shall we three meet again?
                       In thunder, lightning or in rain?
Second witch: When the **hurly-burly's** done.
                       When the battle's lost and won.
First witch: Where the place?
Second witch: Upon the **heath**.
Third witch: There to meet with Macbeth.
All: Fair is foul and foul is fair.
                       Hover through the fog
                       and filthy air!

Exit

Glossary

6

- **hurly-burly**
  confusion/chaos
- **heath** moorland

Find and **copy** the phrase that tells us that the witches' intentions are not good. [1 mark]

_____

Top tips

7

- Read the question carefully and check how many words or phrases it is asking you to copy.
- When it asks for only one word do not copy any other words.
- When it asks you to underline make sure you underline only the relevant words or phrases.
- If you are asked to underline an answer, make sure you use a ruler.

Understanding words in context

To achieve 100 you need to give the meaning of words in **context**.

What you need to know

- Some words or phrases can mean different things depending on the **context** in which they are written.

1 Let's practise

> Ever since humans embarked on the ceaseless quest for knowledge there have been questions that don't really need answers. Yesterday, some of the finest minds in science, engineering and craftsmanship combined to examine one of them anyway: precisely how useless is a chocolate teapot?

[1 mark]

> *Yesterday, some of the finest minds ...*
>
> What does the word *finest* mean in the second sentence?
>
> Tick ✔ **one**.
>
> luxury ☐   smallest ☐
>
> clearest ☐   brightest ☐

1 Read the question and read it again. What is it asking?

The question is asking you to choose an alternative word from a given list.

2 Insert each word in turn in the sentence to replace *finest*. Read the sentence back to yourself each time.

luxury minds   smallest minds
clearest minds   brightest minds

3 Do not stop before the end of the list because you think you may have found the answer. Another word later in the list may be closer in meaning than the one you have chosen.

Yesterday, some of the brightest minds ...

4 Check your answer.

The word that fits the best and is closest in meaning is *brightest*.

Try this

1

> I was hot and dusty and thirsty on the bus, and I thought the journey would never end, but I was happy. I was happy to have arrived, happy not to be seasick any more. Tired though we were, we were buoyed up by the excitement of it all.

What do the words *buoyed up* mean in the last sentence?   [1 mark]

Tick ✔ **one**.

weary   ☐

energised   ☐

bobbing along   ☐

floating   ☐

2

> Aunt Gwen was definitely different! To Jenny, she was evidence that you can be an individual and still have a successful career throughout your life. On the same day that Jenny was 16 and Gwen was 60, they decided to tackle Gwen's photograph album. It was like walking into a paint shop. Aunt Gwen had a different hair colour for every year of her life. One year, emerald green, another, baltic blue. Another year, satsuma orange followed by damson purple. And now, at 60, Gwen had decided to celebrate with a shade of ruby, the symbol for marriage after 40 years. Although the colour hadn't quite turned out to be the shade of ruby she had expected, Gwen was thrilled with the outcome, and Jenny found herself sitting next to a violent shade of red.

*Jenny found herself sitting next to a **violent** shade of red.*

What does the word *violent* mean in the last sentence of this text?   [1 mark]

Tick ✔ **one**.

vicious ☐   brutal ☐   rough ☐   intense ☐

Top tips

- You may be asked to find and copy a word or phrase from the text.
- You may be asked to replace a word or phrase either by writing an alternative word or phrase of your own, or by choosing one from a given list.
- Reread only the part of the text the question refers to. This will save you time.
- Try out all of the words in a given list before choosing which one to use.
- If you are given a list to choose from, some of the words may be trying to trick you – they may be **synonyms** for the original word when it is used in other contexts, but not in this particular context.

2 Let's practise

From humble beginnings in 2005, the group has produced a remarkable number of 'outside art' projects. 'The Hub', an encampment of five large tepees made from 1500 hubcaps, was exhibited at the Eden Project in 2009.

[1 mark]

In this text, the writer uses another word that means *displayed*.

Find and **copy** the word.

1 Read the question and read it again. What is it asking?

The question is asking you to find an alternative word or phrase for *displayed* without changing the meaning of the sentence.

2 *Displayed* is a verb. Why might you want to display something?

You want other people to look at it.

3 Look for clues that tell you what people may want to look at.

art projects

4 Which piece of art is mentioned?

The Hub made out of tepees

5 Read the final sentence about *The Hub* and replace another word with *displayed* where you think it would not change the meaning of the sentence.

... was displayed at the Eden Project ...

6 Check your answer.

The word is *exhibited*.

! Top tips

- Try to think of synonyms for the given word.
- When you think you have found the correct word, replace it with the word given in the question.
- Read the practise sentence again with the given word in place. It must not alter the meaning of the sentence.
- Read the sentences before and after for clues.

Try this

1

> As food passes through your body, it is broken down into pieces small enough to be dissolved in your blood. This process, called digestion, takes place in the digestive tract or alimentary canal – a tube that runs from your mouth to a hole in your bottom called the anus. Food is broken down physically by chewing and churning, and chemically by the action of digestive juices, made by organs called glands.
>
> Food is chewed in the mouth and mixed with a digestive juice called saliva, which is made in your salivary glands. Saliva moistens the food so it slides down your throat easily.

The phrase *broken down* is used twice in this text.   [1 mark]
Which other word or phrase could replace *broken down*?

_____

2

> It was a majestic hall, with wooden towers and pinnacles that reached higher than the highest trees. It was the tallest, finest building that had ever been seen in the land. And the king was proud of it. Nothing as grand had existed in his kingdom before. It became known as the Great Hall.
>
> As soon as the Hall was finished, the party began. It was to be the feast to end all feasts. It began one morning as the sun rose and then continued day after day, night after night. Long tables sagged under the weight of the food, and revellers sagged under the effect of the drink. It made their heads spin and caused them to sing louder and louder and to dance more and more wildly.

Find and **copy** the word meaning *partygoers*.   [1 mark]

_____

3

> All my earliest memories are very like dreams. I know that none of them are proper memories, none that I could really call my own anyway. I feel I've come out of half-forgotten, half-remembered times, and I'm sure I've often filled the half-forgotten times with made-up memories. Perhaps it's my mind trying to make some sense of the unknown. So I can't know for certain where the made-up ones end and the real ones begin. All the earliest childhood memories must be like that for everyone I suppose, but maybe mine are more blurred than most, and maybe that's because I have no family stories to support them, no hard facts, no real evidence, no certificates, not a single photograph.

Find and **copy one** word or phrase that shows that the narrator's memories   [1 mark]
aren't as clear as they could be.

_____

Explaining words in context

To achieve 100 you need to explain the meaning of words in **context**.

 What you need to know

- Some words or phrases can mean different things depending on the context in which they are written.
- Quotes from the text can be used to support your answer.
- Questions may require understanding of synonyms or antonyms.

Let's practise

One day, my attention was drawn to many insects and some lizards rushing across a bare piece of ground. A little way behind, every stalk and leaf was blackened by ants. The **swarm** divided itself and descended an old wall. By this means they surrounded many insects; the efforts the poor little creatures made to extricate themselves from such a death were wonderful.

 Glossary

- **swarm** collective noun for a group of insects

What does the verb *extricate* tell you about the actions of the other insects?

[1 mark]

1	Read the question and read it again. What is it asking?	The question is asking you to explain the meaning of *extricate*.
2	What do we know about the other insects? Read around the sentence.	They are surrounded by ants. They don't want to die.
3	In this situation, what might they want to do?	They might try to get out or escape.
4	Write these words in the sentence to see if they make sense.	The efforts the poor little creatures made to escape from such a death were wonderful.
5	Answer the question. Then, check your answer.	*Extricate* tells me that the creatures are trying to escape or get away from the ants.

Top tips

- Look to see if the definition of the word or phrase is in the text.
- Pay attention to the words around it. Sometimes, these words will tell you the definition or give you clues about the definition.

Try this

1

> If only she'd go, thought Theo. If only the blizzard would turn away and let her go back to where she came from. If only Dad were here. He turned to the shepherd clock, wishing its hands would tell him it was morning and there was still a chance that the day would be fine, and a mysterious stranger wouldn't be forced to shelter in their home.
>
> How can I tell if our guest is a witch, wondered Theo, if witches hardly ever cry? Once again he felt the clocks hesitate, and there was a curious bend in time, a tock-ticking, unwinding of confused springs and **pendulums**. And the thought of his father, whose heart beat like a clock. Why hadn't he phoned? Was he caught somewhere on an icy road, or lost on the moor and slowly freezing?

Glossary
- **pendulum** a long, heavy weight that swings backwards and forwards on a clock

What does the word *confused* tell you about the movement of the clocks' springs and pendulums?   [2 marks]

_____

_____

2

> While the majority of diagnoses of **myopia** in children used to happen around puberty, increasing numbers of children are needing glasses younger and younger.
>
> And it's children from comfortable backgrounds who are driving this increase. Why? In part, because they are wealthy enough to have access to all those seductive screens and gadgets, says Joanne Hancox, a consultant in **paediatrics** at London's Moorfields Eye Hospital.

Glossary
- **myopia** short-sightedness
- **paediatrics** branch of medicine for babies, children and young people

Why has the word *seductive* been used to describe screens and gadgets?   [1 mark]

_____

_____

3

> Eva's report was, as it always was, first rate and outstanding. She had worked hard in her first school and now she was proving to be a big hit too at her new secondary school. Eva liked to show off and brag about her grades. You could never say that Eva or her work was inconspicuous.
>
> The trouble was, Eva was not impressed with her report. She always focused on things she didn't do so well and now she was dwelling on the comment, 'Eva likes music lessons'. To Eva, 'like' wasn't good enough!

Use evidence from the text to explain why *You could never say that Eva or her work was inconspicuous.*   [1 mark]

_____

_____

Retrieving and recording information

To achieve 100 you need to **find** and **record** information in fiction and non-fiction texts.

What you need to know

- Questions may begin with words such as *who, why, what, where, when, how.*
- **Retrieving** information is not a test of memory. The answers will be in the text.

1 Let's practise

Once again, the **sanctuary** that is Tiggywinkles echoes to the sound of the builders and their mini-monster machines. There is constantly the need to expand our small plot of **rural** Buckinghamshire, to give both the patients and staff modern facilities. We need to reflect the ever-changing experiences of our animals and the staff that care for them.

After open areas were created, a hedgehog enclosure was built to incorporate the hedgehog maternity unit, which the nurses christened 'Hogwarts'.

Now it is time for fences to be renewed to partition eight large hedgehog **recuperation** pens into smaller ones. As the hospital gets busier, every inch of space is crucial. This new hedgehog area will be a welcome addition.

Glossary

- **sanctuary** place of safety
- **rural** countryside
- **recuperation** recovery, usually after an illness or accident

The building work at Tiggywinkles is to improve facilities for patients and staff.
Who are the *patients* and *staff* at Tiggywinkles?

[1 mark]

1 Read the question and read it again. What is it asking?	**The question is asking you to explain who the patients and staff are at Tiggywinkles.**
2 Locate the words in the text. Where are they?	**They are in the second sentence.**
3 Read on and look for clues.	**The following sentence says *our animals and the staff*, so the patients are animals.**
4 Read on to find out which animals are patients.	**They are hedgehogs.**

The word *staff* is in the question, so don't repeat it. Find out who they are or what they do by reading ahead.

The next sentence mentions *nurses*.

 Answer the question using evidence or quote from the text. Then, check your answer.

The patients are hedgehogs and the staff are the nurses who care for them.

Try this

1

Choose your kit carefully. You will need a strong tent, warm sleeping bag and a mat for camping. You should include tools such as a snow shovel, and a signalling kit in case you get into difficulties. Travel games will come in handy if bad weather keeps you in your tent! You'll need ski poles and skis or snowshoes to move over snowy terrain. An ice axe and crampons are useful to scale icy slopes. Wearing the right clothing can make the difference between life and death in polar regions. Wearing lots of layers is the key to keeping warm.

Don't skimp on quality when it comes to essentials for a polar trip. Your kit needs to be tough to withstand the harshest conditions on Earth!

Why should you choose equipment carefully for a trip to the Arctic? **[2 marks]**
Give **two** reasons.

1. _____

2. _____

2

Frogs have been disappearing at an alarming rate in recent decades. Habitat destruction is the main cause of decrease in lowland areas, and climate change is the main cause of extinction in mountainous regions.

Frogs are under serious threat from global warming which can act to raise cloud levels in tropical cloud forests. As the clouds rise, the frogs at the newly exposed lower levels lose their habitat as the soil dries, and their eggs can dry up and die. Some frog species live only on a single mountain range, or even on a single mountain, so when problems arise the entire species can easily become extinct.

Why are frogs *disappearing at an alarming rate*? Give **two** reasons. **[2 marks]**

1. _____

2. _____

Top tips

- **Skim** the text for a few seconds before you close-read a second time.
- **Scan** the text and pick out key details.
- Find the information you need and copy it.
- Check that you have answered the correct question (e.g. *who, what, why, when, where, how*).

2 Let's practise

Hundreds of years ago, the Tower of London was used to hold important prisoners. Only royal prisoners had their heads chopped off there, including Anne Boleyn in 1536 and Catherine Howard in 1542 – both were wives of Henry VIII.

In 1671, Captain Blood attempted to steal the Crown Jewels from the Tower. At this time alligators were kept in the moat, which wasn't drained until 1845.

The Tower became famous for keeping many animals. In 1816, George III was given a grizzly bear to add to the collection.

Unfortunately animals sometimes escaped and attacked people, so the animals were sent to London Zoo in 1832.

[1 mark]

Draw a line to match each event to the date it happened.

Event	Date
A grizzly bear lived in the Tower.	• 1536
Anne Boleyn was beheaded.	• 1816
Alligators were kept in the moat.	• 1845
The moat of the Tower was drained.	• 1671

1 Read the question and read it again. What is it asking?

The question is asking you to match each date to the correct event from the text.

2 Read each of the events and the dates in the question, then find the first date in the text.

It is 1536 and it is in the second sentence.

3 Read the sentence in which it is written to identify the event it refers to.

It refers to Anne Boleyn being beheaded. Draw a line from this event to 1536.

4 Repeat the process for the other dates in the text. Are any unclear?

The sentence containing the date 1671 does not describe any of the events listed in the question.

5 Read the sentence after this one.

The next sentence begins *At this time alligators were kept in the moat*. That is one of the events listed in the question.

6 Have you drawn four lines? What is your answer?

A grizzly bear lived in the Tower.	• 1536
Anne Boleyn was beheaded.	• 1816
Alligators were kept in the moat.	• 1845
The moat of the Tower was drained.	• 1671

7 Check your answer.

Try this

1

> LEGO building blocks were created by Ole Kirk Christiansen, a Danish man whose company made wooden toys. In 1934 Ole named his business 'LEg GOdt,' which means 'play well' in Danish. In 1947 a special machine was made that could make large quantities of interlocking plastic blocks. By 1949 the new machine was making about 200 different kinds of toys. In 1953, the blocks were called 'LEGO bricks' and, in 1958, a new design meant they looked like the LEGO bricks we know today. In the same year, Godtfred Christiansen became head of LEGO following the death of his father. In the 1960s, LEGO toys were being sold in countries all over the world including the United Kingdom, France and Sweden. By popular demand, other countries soon started selling the toys, including the United States in 1973.

Draw a line to match each LEGO event to the date it happened.　　[1 mark]

Event		Date
Godtfred Christiansen became head of the LEGO company. •		• 1953
Two hundred kinds of toys were being manufactured. •		• 1958
The company was named LEg GOdt. •		• 1949
Toys were made for the United States. •		• 1934
The bricks were called LEGO bricks. •		• 1973

2

> J.K. Rowling was born on July 31, 1965. She is an international bestselling author, known for the Harry Potter series of books. Her first book, *Harry Potter and the Philosopher's Stone*, was published in 1997. Following the success of this book, Rowling wrote her second book, *Harry Potter and the Chamber of Secrets*, published in 1998. Book three in the series, *Harry Potter and the Prisoner of Azkaban*, followed in 1999 and, in 2000, book four, *Harry Potter and the Goblet of Fire* became the fastest-selling book in history. The books were translated into many different languages. Rowling continued the series with *Harry Potter and the Order of the Phoenix* in 2003 and, two years later, *Harry Potter and the Half-Blood Prince*. The final book in the series, *Harry Potter and the Deathly Hallows*, was published in 2007.

Draw a line to match each event with the correct date.　　[1 mark]

Event		Date
Harry Potter and the Order of the Phoenix was published. •		• 2007
The first Harry Potter book was published. •		• 2000
J.K. Rowling was born. •		• 1997
Harry Potter and the Deathly Hallows was released. •		• 2003
The fourth book became the fastest-selling book in history. •		• 1965

3 Let's practise

The main courtyard was filled with warriors – mermen with fish tails from the waist down and human bodies from the waist up, except their skin was blue, which I'd never known before. Some were tending the wounded. Some were sharpening spears and swords. One passed us, swimming in a hurry. His eyes were bright green, like that stuff they put in glow sticks, and his teeth were shark teeth.

Complete the table about the warriors.

[2 marks]

Who were the warriors?	
What was different about their skin?	
Which part of his body was compared to the stuff they put in glow sticks?	

1 Read the question and read it again. What is it asking?

The question is asking you to complete the table about the warriors. The first question is who were the warriors?

2 Read the text.

The first line of the text says the warriors were mermen. Write 'mermen' in the first answer box.

3 What is the second question in the table asking?

What was different about their skin?

4 Keep reading the text until you find where it talks about their skin.

It says their skin was blue and that is different to usual. Write 'it was blue'.

5 What is the last question asking and where can you find it?

It is asking which part of his body is compared to the stuff they put in glow sticks. It is in the last line: *His eyes were bright green, like the stuff they put in glow sticks.* So the answer is 'his eyes'.

6 Check your answers.

Try this

1

Take the whisper of the river,	The rumble of the storm cloud,
The thunder of the sea,	The singing of the sun,
The echo of the songbird,	The music of the moonrise,
The rustle of the tree,	And mix them one by one,
The howling of the blizzard,	Till all the notes are silver
The purring of the cat,	And all the chords are gold,
The shudder of the earthquake,	Then give your gift of laughter
The whistle of the gnat,	To the sick, the sad, the old.

Complete the table using the poem.   *[2 marks]*

What noise does the blizzard make?	
What does the poem say makes music?	
Who does the poem suggest that you should give your laughter to?	

2

And neither of them stumbled and the candles didn't go out, and at last they came to where they could see a little door in the brick wall on their right. There was no bolt or handle on this side of it, of course, for the door had been made for getting in, not for getting out; but there was a catch (as there often is on the inside of a cupboard door) which they felt sure they would be able to turn.

Both felt that it was becoming very serious, but neither would draw back. Then, with a great shock, they saw that they were looking, not into a deserted attic, but into a **furnished** room. But it seemed empty enough. It was dead silent. Polly's curiosity got the better of her. She blew out her candle and stepped out into the strange room, making no more noise than a mouse.

Glossary

- **furnished** filled with furniture

Using information from the text, tick ✔ **true** or **false** in the following table to explain what the children did in the story.   *[1 mark]*

	True	False
They stumbled in the darkness.		
They used the handle to open the little door.		
The looked into a furnished room.		
Polly was very quiet when she stepped into the room.		

Identifying key details

To achieve 100 you need to identify the **key details** in a text.

What you need to know

- Within a text, every paragraph has a key concept or main idea. The main ideas in a text are the most important pieces of information the writer wants you to know.
- The key details in a text are the words, phrases or sentences that communicate the main ideas.
- When using key details you can quote directly from the text, using inverted commas, or paraphrase (use your own words).

1 Let's practise

Grendel lived in the fens and the foul-smelling marshland beyond the forest. The marsh was littered with oozing pools and the festering remains of dead otters and decaying fish. No one, not even the bravest warrior, went there. The place reeked of evil.

Evil suited Grendel. Half man, half fiend, he was an extraordinary creature with supernatural strength. Covered in a green, horny skin that no sword could cut through, he came from a race of sea monsters, giants, goblins and other outcasts from the human race.

Grendel was in the habit of sleeping for centuries, and he had been asleep so long that the king and his **subjects** had forgotten his existence. If they thought of him at all, they remembered him as a creature from legends. That was their big mistake.

Glossary

- **subject** person living under the rule of a king or queen

Top tips

- Use skimming and scanning to locate key details that may be repeated within a paragraph or across paragraphs.
- You may be asked to order events from the text, or select the most appropriate summary from a given list.
- Do not include your own opinion or add extra information.

The main idea in this text is that Grendel is a *monster*. Give **two** details that support this idea.

[2 marks]

1 Read the question and read it again. What is it asking?

The question is asking you to find the key details that support the main idea of the text.

2 How does the writer communicate the idea that Grendel is a monster?

The writer uses descriptive language.

3 Scan the text and look for key details that describe a monster.

lives in foul-smelling marshland; half man, half fiend; tough, green, horny skin; supernatural strength

4 Choose two of the details for the answer. Quote directly from the text if you want to or write the answer in your own words. Then, check your answer.

He is *covered in a green, horny skin*. He is *half man, half fiend*.

Try this

1

> Roald Dahl LOVED chocolate – he had a little red box full of small chocolate bars, which he would bring out every day after dinner. Roald Dahl loved chocolate so much that he started keeping the foil wrappers from all the bars he ate, turning them into a ball. He continued to add to the ball, which stayed on his desk in his writing hut until he died!

This text tells you that Roald Dahl *loved chocolate*.

[2 marks]

Write **two** key details that support this.

1. _____

2. _____

2

> When playing some sports, athletes are required to wear special shoes. Two such sports are golf and bowling. Golf shoes have sharp metal spikes called cleats. These cleats help golfers keep their footing while swinging the club. On the other end of the spectrum are bowling shoes, which are very smooth and have almost no traction at all. Bowling shoes help bowlers slide down the lane while throwing the ball. While both of these types of shoes help athletes perform, it is not advisable to wear either of them outside except for sports. Golf shoes and bowling shoes do not have soles that are fit for street use.

Write **one** sentence to **summarise** the main idea in this text.

[1 mark]

_____

_____

Let's practise

The luxurious fashions shown in Elizabethan artwork most often reflect the clothing worn by royalty, the **nobility** and the **elite**.

As in the Middle Ages, the fabrics used to create **garments** for the Elizabethans were wool and linen.

The upper classes wore garments made of silk, satin, velvet, damask and taffeta, in addition to wool and linen.

Finer linens were bleached in the sun, embroidered or block printed. Fashionable decorations included embroidery, lace and gems or pearls sewn onto the fabric.

The fashionable elite used whale bone (baleen) stiffening, willow wood or steel in their **bodices**.

 Glossary

- **nobility** upper class
- **elite** privileged
- **garments** clothes
- **bodice** woman's undergarment laced at the front

[2 marks]

The paragraphs above describe Elizabethan fashion for rich people.
Find and **copy two** phrases or sentences to support this.

1	Read the question and read it again. What is it asking?	The question is asking you to find two key details that support the idea that the text is about **rich people's fashions.**
2	Look for other key words that mean rich people across the paragraphs. Use your knowledge of synonyms to help.	Words include *royalty, nobility, elite.*
3	What do the paragraphs tell you about the fashion for these people?	They wore things like silk, satin and taffeta.
4	Look through the other paragraphs for further key details.	Their clothes had decorations that would be expensive. They used whale bone in their bodices.
5	Choose two key words or phrases to support the evidence that the clothing is for rich people. Write each separately.	1 The upper classes wore silk, satin and taffeta. 2 The fashionable elite used whale bone.
6	Check your answer.	

Try this

1

Fossils are the **preserved** remains of plants or animals. To be considered fossils, scientists have decided they have to be over 10,000 years old.

First, the body of the animal or plant is usually buried under something soft such as sand or soil. Next, water fills the inside of the body and the soft parts rot away. Finally, the hard parts, such as the skeleton, are left behind.

Over millions of years, the sand and mud build up in layers and eventually turn to rock with the preserved remains of the plant or animal, called a FOSSIL, inside. What was once bone is now rock in the shape of a bone.

Glossary

- **preserved** found in good condition after a long time

[1 mark]

The title of this text is *How Fossils Are Formed*.
Underline **two** key details from the text that show how fossils are formed.

2

Then, as Miranda fell into a charmed sleep, the source of Prospero's magical **tempest** appeared.

This was Ariel, a strange creature who seemed all made of fire and air, and who was visible only to Prospero. Ariel's special quality was to 'fly,

To swim, to dive into the fire, to ride
On the curled clouds...'

Ariel had been on the island before Prospero arrived, but had been imprisoned in a tree by a witch. He was in pain and misery because it was his very nature to be free, to ride the elements high in the sky, or deep in the earth and below the sea's surface; he could create both roaring storms and healing, soothing music. When Prospero discovered Ariel in the tree he set him free, but on condition he should serve him for twelve years, according to his swift and airy nature.

Glossary

- **tempest** storm

[2 marks]

This narrative describes Prospero's magical helper, Ariel.
Give **two** details to support the idea that Ariel is magical.

1. _____

2. _____

Summarising main ideas

To achieve 100 you need to summarise the **main ideas** in a text.

✓ What you need to know

- Within a text, every paragraph has a key concept or main idea. The main ideas in a text are the most important pieces of information the writer wants you to know.

1 Let's practise

In 1947, the *Studebaker Starlight* started a trend for sleek, stylish cars. The following year, a designer working for the Cadillac car company was inspired when a fighter jet flew by. American designers used every trick to make their cars stand out, from stylish fins and shiny chrome bumpers to dazzling paintwork and pointed tail-lights.

Most impressive of all were the stretch limos. Still popular today, they are twice the length of a normal car, with plush leather seats and a drinks bar inside. The rich and famous love to travel by limo. They can soak up the sights in chauffeur-driven luxury, while mirrored windows stop excited fans from seeing in.

[1 mark]

What is the main idea in this text? Tick ✔ **one** box.

American cars are popular. ☐

American car designs stand out from other cars. ☐

The stretch limo is the most impressive American-designed car. ☐

American car designs are inspired by fighter jets. ☐

1 Read the question and read it again. What is it asking?

The question is asking you to choose one answer that most closely fits the main idea of the text.

2 Read all the choices given. Find evidence in the text that American cars are popular.

The text tells you that the stretch limo is popular. It doesn't mention other popular cars, so discount the first answer choice.

3 Do American cars stand out from others as given in the second choice?

Yes. They have *stylish fins, shiny chrome bumpers, dazzling paintwork and pointed tail-lights*. However, the text does not give any further detail about these features, so it is not the *main idea* of the text.

4 Look at the two choices you have left. Is it possible to eliminate one of them?

The last choice can be eliminated because we only know that one car designer was inspired by a fighter jet.

5 Reread the text to make sure that you are confident the third choice is the main idea of the text. Then tick the correct box.

The main idea is that the stretch limo is the most impressive American car.

6 Check your answer.

Try this

1

> Frowning, Jess held her wrist to the moonlight to peer at her watch. Ten minutes had become twenty. So what? It wouldn't feel so long in daylight. It wouldn't feel so long in a crowded noisy bar. Here in the eerie shadows of the ancient temple ruins it was easy to get spooked, that was all.
>
> OK. She was starting to get cross now. *A bit late* didn't mean he had any right to leave her standing here in the darkness. For thirty minutes now!
>
> It wasn't so great in the dark in the shifting moon shadows that made a monster out of every massive tree, a stalking horror out of every unseen animal.
>
> *Forty-seven minutes!* Time to go.

What is the main idea in this text?   [1 mark]

Tick ✔ one.

The temple was dark and scary.	☐
Jess had been waiting a long time.	☐
Jess wanted to leave.	☐
Jess had been waiting for a short while.	☐

Top tips

- Look for key details in the text that support the question or choices provided.
- Reject answer choices where the clues are absent or limited in the text.
- To be sure you have made the correct choice, read through the text one final time.

2 Let's practise

Most of the world's roller coasters are gravity-powered, which means that once a motor has dragged the cars up to the top of the first big hill, it's only the force of gravity that takes you all the way to the end of the ride.

The force that pushes you down into your seat on a roller coaster is called the centripetal force. The need to have enough centripetal force is why a roller coaster's loops aren't circular. Instead, they're what's known as clothoid loops, which look like a circle that someone's squeezed from the sides. As you climb up the loop, you lose speed. In order to keep enough centripetal force to hold you in your seat, you have to tighten up the radius of the loop.

What is the most important thing this text tells you about roller coasters?

[1 mark]

1	Read the question and read it again. What is it asking?	**The question is asking you to explain the main idea of the text.**
2	Are any terms repeated throughout the text?	**Yes, *force* – the force of gravity and centripetal force.**
3	How does gravity help during the ride?	**It keeps the cars going to the end of the ride.**
4	How does centripetal force help during the ride?	**It keeps you in your seat.**
5	Put the information together and answer the question.	**Roller coasters use two forces, gravity to keep the ride going and centripetal force to keep you safely in your seat.**
6	Check your answer.	

! Top tips

- Look for key details in the text that relate to the question.
- Identify words or phrases that are repeated.
- Make the link between key details and repeated words or phrases.
- Use key details in your answer.

Try this

1

Every day Gabriela followed the **shaman** through the forest and learned about the hundreds of plants he used for medicines; plants to cure earaches and stomach aches, snake and insect bites.

One day Nahtahlah noticed Gabriela scratching her elbow. Going over to a weedee tree, he peeled the bark away. He spread the bright red **sap** on Gabriela's arm. By the next day the fungus and itching had disappeared.

After several months Gabriela left. But every year she returned to Kwamala to learn more and more of the shaman's wisdom.

 Glossary

- **shaman** a person who uses ancient healing traditions for cures
- **sap** sugary liquid produced by plants

[1 mark]

What is the most important thing this text tells you about the forest?

_____

_____

2

Robinson spent part of each day sorting his **booty** and storing it away properly in the cave. He also improved his shelter, raising the fence and making a ladder to get in and out, and building a kind of big, wooden porch for the cave entrance with timber from the ship. And in between doing all that, he and Toby explored as much of the island as possible.

'I think we're going to be fine, Toby,' Robinson said as they were heading home late one afternoon. It was the twelfth day since the wreck. 'It's not such a scary place as I thought. There aren't any dangerous wild animals here, just lots of goats, and I can hunt them for meat. I might even be able to catch a few and keep them for their milk. And there are fish in the lagoon, so Freckles and Rufus can have the occasional treat.'

That evening, Robinson sat in his cave surrounded by his supplies in their neat piles, his tools and weapons all neatly arranged too.

Glossary

- **booty** valuable stolen goods

[1 mark]

What is Robinson trying to do?
Explain in **one** sentence.

_____

_____

Making inferences

To achieve 100 you need to make **inferences** from the text.

✓ What you need to know

- Writers often use clues to imply meaning in texts.
- A good reader works like a detective, using these clues to work out missing information. You need to add this information to what you already know in order to make sense of the text.
- Give evidence or use quotes if they support your answer.

1 Let's practise

I remember the Captain as if it were yesterday, as he came plodding to the inn door, his sea chest following behind in a hand-barrow, a tall, strong, heavy, nut-brown man, his **tarry** pigtail falling over the shoulder of his soiled blue coat, his hands ragged and scarred, with black, broken nails, and the sabre cut across one cheek, a dirty, livid white.

🔍 Glossary

- **tarry** coated in tar

What does the Captain's appearance tell you about his character? Give **two** examples.

[2 marks]

1	Read the question and read it again. What is it asking?	The question is asking you to infer the Captain's character from the information about his appearance.
2	What does the text tell you about the Captain's appearance?	He is tall with brown skin. His clothes are dirty. His hands are ragged and scarred. He has a scar across his cheek.
3	Do you think this is the usual appearance of a captain?	Captains are usually well dressed and clean.
4	What do the scars tell you?	He has been involved in fights.
5	Answer the question about the Captain's character with evidence from the text.	1. He doesn't care about how he looks because he is dirty. It says his coat is soiled, and his hands are ragged and scarred, with black, broken nails.
6	Check your answer.	2. He is a fighter because he has scars on his cheek and on his hands.

28

Try this

1
> The dragons thrashed around wildly in the surf, gagging and choking, with their eyes popping, their tails causing such tidal waves that the boys were soaked, even though they were scrambling away from the headland as fast as they could.
>
> Finally, with some last heaving shudders and grim gurgles, both mighty beasts lay still in the water.
>
> There was silence.
>
> The boys stopped running. They stood gasping for breath, watching the motionless beasts with dread. The boys' dragons, which were flying some way ahead of the boys, also turned, and hung still in the air.

Why do you think the boys watched the dragons *with dread*?　　　　[1 mark]

_____

_____

_____

2
> One Careful Owner (rumoured to be
> Queen **Boudicca** of the Iceni)
> Low Mileage
> Two or Four **Horsepower**
> Wheels with Sharp Knives (if required)
> 5 months Road Tax
> Blood-Red Bodywork
> inlaid with Roman Bones

Glossary
- **Boudicca** queen of the Celtic Iceni, a tribe living in the East of England before the Roman invasion
- **horsepower** an old-fashioned measurement of power

What does the description of the chariot tell you about its condition?　　[2 marks]
Give **two** examples.

1. _____

2. _____

Top tips

- Be a detective. Find clues that help you fill in the missing information.
- Put all the clues together and add them to the information you know.
- Try to empathise with a central character. What would you do? How would you feel?
- Use a quote from the text or use your own words to support your answer.

2 Let's practise

Monday	Tuesday
Polished my scales	Measured my wings
till they shone like the sea.	on the door of the cave
Pity Ma won't let me paint my claws.	still only a measly ten feet long.
Tried trampling the ground –	I'm trying to master
it didn't look bad, but	that flick of the tail
I'm not too happy about my roars.	that knocks a knight down, however strong.

[1 mark]

From this poem, you can tell that ...

Tick ✔ one.

the narrator is an adult dragon. ☐
the mother is easygoing. ☐
the narrator has a good roar. ☐
the narrator is not confident. ☐

1 Read the question and read it again. What is it asking?

The question is asking you to infer one thing about the poem.

2 Read the poem again. Read all the choices then look at the first choice again. Does the poem tell you who the narrator is?

No. I will need to use inference to answer the question.

3 Gather any clues that tell you the narrator may be an adult dragon.

It does not. It gives clues that it is a young dragon such as it wants to paint its claws and measure its wings.

4 You can eliminate the first choice. Read on. Is the mother easygoing?

No. She won't let the narrator paint its claws.

5 Does the dragon have a good roar?

No. It is not happy about its roar.

6 Is there any evidence that the dragon is not confident?

It says its wings aren't long enough and that it's trying to master knocking down a knight which means it can't do it yet.

7 Eliminate the first three choices and tick the last one.

the narrator is not confident.

8 Check you have ticked one box.

Try this

1

Are your children peaky and thin?
Too many late nights? Too much telly?
Forest air and a fattening diet
Will very soon put things right.

A week or two at Sweetmeat Cottage
Is bound to make them scrumptiously chubby.
Children just love my gingerbread house,
My liquorice doors and chimneys.

There's everything here to delight a child,
And one kind lady to see to their needs –
For I love children, tasty little darlings!
Apply without delay.

What are the intentions of the narrator of this poem? Tick ✔ one.   *[1 mark]*

To look after children. ☐

To give parents a break. ☐

To eat children. ☐

To give children a holiday. ☐

2

At first it may seem odd that people would want to live close to a volcano. After all, volcanoes have a nasty habit of exploding, discharging liquid rock, ash, poisonous gases and generally doing things that kill people. Yet, throughout history, people have deliberately chosen to risk all those hazards and live near them, even on the slopes of active volcanoes that have erupted within living memory.

After thousands of years, volcanic rocks become rich in minerals and when they break down they form rich soils. Farmers are able to grow a wide variety of produce including grapes, vegetables, orange and lemon trees and herbs.

The heat from underground steam is used to drive turbines and produce electricity, or to heat water supplies that are then used to provide household heating and hot water. In addition, tourism creates jobs in shops, restaurants, hotels, tourist centres and national parks.

Why do people choose to live near volcanoes?   *[1 mark]*

Tick ✔ one.

Volcanoes are dangerous but attractive. ☐

Fertile soil is created as a result of volcanic eruptions. ☐

People use the liquids and gases from volcanoes. ☐

Houses, roads and buildings can be covered with ash. ☐

Explaining inferences

To achieve 100 you need to explain **inferences** and justify them with evidence from the text.

What you need to know

- Writers often use clues to imply meaning in texts.
- A good reader works like a detective, using these clues to find out missing information. You need to add this information to what you already know in order to make sense of the text.
- Include both the clues and your conclusion in your answer.
- There can be more than one correct answer when explaining **inferences**.

1 Let's practise

> The birds sat on the trees and sang so sweetly that the children used to stop their games in order to listen to them. 'How happy we are here!' they cried to each other.
>
> One day the Giant came back. When he arrived he saw the children playing in the garden.
>
> 'What are you doing here?' he cried in a very gruff voice and the children ran away.
>
> 'My own garden is my own garden,' said the Giant; 'anyone can understand that, and I will allow nobody to play in it but myself.' So he built a high wall all round it, and put up a notice-board: TRESPASSERS WILL BE PROSECUTED.

What can we infer about the giant's character? Explain fully, referring to the text in your answer.

[3 marks]

1 Read the question and read it again. What is it asking?

The question is asking you to infer the giant's character, and explain your thoughts.

2 Find clues to tell you about the giant.

He builds a wall and puts up a notice so the children keep away. He talks to the children in a *gruff* voice.

3 What do these clues tell you?

He is scary, mean and selfish.

4 Answer the question with your ideas and the clues you have found. Then check your answer.

The giant is selfish and mean because he wants to keep the garden all to himself. He put up a high wall and a sign, and frightened the children away.

Try this

1

> Splat! The coleslaw tub fell right in front of Mum's feet as she opened the fridge door. Splat! Splat! Splat! The butter, milk and leftover lasagne followed quickly behind.
>
> Mum stopped and turned round, her dripping wet coat making even more mess on the floor. She'd arrived just in time to miss the worst of the storm.
>
> What on earth could have happened? It looked like she'd been burgled by a hungry visitor.
>
> She turned around to look at the kitchen bench. Empty pizza boxes, a sharp knife, pools of coke flowing dangerously near the edge. She scooped up a gooey red liquid and tasted it. Mmm! Definitely strawberry doughnut jam; George's favourite. But George was at Scout Camp wasn't he? He wasn't due home until tomorrow morning. Besides, there was far too much food here for one person alone.
>
> Without making a sound, Mum silently inched towards the kitchen door…

What conclusions had Mum come to?   *[2 marks]*

Give **two** conclusions, referring to the text in your answer.

1. _____

2. _____

2

Woodland racer
Acorn chaser

Tree shaker
Acorn taker

Nut cracker
Acorn snacker

Sky rider
Acorn hider

Winter snoozer
Acorn loser

Spring reminder
Acorn finder

What do you think the title of this poem might be? *[3 marks]*

Explain your answer, referring to the text.

_____

_____

_____

_____

_____

Top tips

- Ask yourself, 'What did I think about that?', 'What information did I use to think that?' and find clues in the text to support your thinking. You may need to change your original thoughts if the clues to support them aren't there in the text.
- You should answer with as much detail as possible as there may be more marks for more than one answer.

2 Let's practise

Society's **perception** of clean versus dirty has varied throughout ancient and modern history. In the Elizabethan **era**, it was not **uncommon** for people to bathe fewer than 10 times a year. According to written accounts, Elizabeth I declared that she only bathed once a month.

Most people wore the same outfit for days and days in a row. Laundry was done maybe once a year, if at all. Many people wore pomanders, hollow balls filled with dried herbs and flowers, to ward off the smell.

The Elizabethans didn't have toothpaste and weren't very good about cleaning their teeth. Many had rotten teeth and very bad breath. It is said that the reason Elizabeth I never smiled for portraits was because her teeth looked so bad.

Glossary

- **perception** view
- **era** period in history
- **uncommon** unusual

What impression does the text give you about the hygiene of the Elizabethans? Explain your answer fully, referring to the text.

[3 marks]

1 Read the question and read it again. What is it asking?

The question is asking you to use information in the text to explain your thoughts on the Elizabethans' cleanliness.

2 Find evidence in the text to tell you what they had to wash.

They had to wash their clothes, bodies and teeth.

3 Did they wash these things often?

They bathed fewer than 10 times a year, washed clothes once a year if at all, and weren't good at cleaning teeth.

4 Are these the habits of clean people? What can you infer?

They tell me that they were not clean or didn't care about cleanliness.

5 Put your thoughts together with the evidence. Explain in two or more sentences if you can.

I don't think the Elizabethans were very clean people. They didn't bathe very often. They hardly ever washed their clothes and they had bad teeth, which means that they probably didn't brush them enough.

6 Check your answer.

Try this

1

> **Study maths and science for space jobs, urges astronaut**
>
> An astronaut has called for more children to study maths and science so they are prepared for a future boom in space-related jobs.
>
> James F Reilly, who completed three space missions and now works for the Kennedy Space Centre, predicted space tourism will become routine and trips to Mars will be possible within the lifetime of today's schoolchildren. To prepare them he said it is vital that they study STEM subjects – science, technology, engineering and maths.
>
> He added that today's schoolchildren should plan to get jobs in space-related industries, rather than computer programming and app development.
>
> Mr Reilly, 61, flew from his home in Colorado to the UK to speak to children and told them it is important that girls take STEM subjects as well as boys.
>
> He said: "My sister is much smarter at maths than me. It is not a gender-limited capability. Don't listen to the culture that says it is a boys' subject."
>
> He added: "Space tourism will be normal within an eight-year-old's lifetime. I think visiting Mars will be possible. It will be like visiting Antarctica is now – an adventure destination."

Explain why studying STEM subjects is vital for the future.   *[1 mark]*

_____

_____

2

> But it was Joey Father loved best. If ever he got sick, Father would bed down with him in his stable and never leave his side. He loved that horse like a brother, more maybe. Anyway, one day, a few months after the war started, Father goes off to market to sell some fat sheep. In them days of course, you had to drive them down the road to market. No lorries, nothing like that. So he was gone most of the day. Meanwhile the army's come to the village looking for good sturdy horses, and they're paying good money too. They needed all the horses they could get for the cavalry, for pulling the guns maybe, or the ammunition wagons, ambulances too. Most things were horse-drawn in them days. Father comes back from market, and sees Joey being taken away. It's too late to stop it. It was his own father that did it. He'd gone and sold Joey to the army for forty pounds.

Explain how Father might have felt when he discovered his horse had been sold.   *[3 marks]*

Use evidence from the text to support your answer.

_____

_____

_____

Predicting

To achieve 100 you need to **predict** what might happen next in a text.

✔ What you need to know

- Sometimes information in a text is stated outright and sometimes it is only implied.
- Good readers use clues in the text to explain what might happen next.
- **Prediction** questions are usually based on fiction texts.
- Your answers should refer to the plot, characters or events that have happened.
- Your answers should be written with detail, in one or two sentences, supported by evidence from the text.

Let's practise

Grendel hated the music. He hated it because he hated the humans that made it. He hated it with a hatred that burnt bright as a star. He hated it as only a demon can hate. It reminded him of what an outcast he was. In his ears, that music sounded like the buzzing of flies.

Why should people be happy, he wondered. Why should they make music and sing and hold great feasts while he sat alone in a stinking bog? He was full of jealousy and hatred. The king had left his favourite warriors to guard the Hall, but because there was peace in the land they did not take their guard duty seriously. They fell asleep, and did not hear Grendel croaking his terrible song as he moved out from the shadows towards them:

'Sweet human meat's the best to eat,

And human bones the best to grind.'

What might Grendel do when he arrives at the Hall? Explain fully, referring to the text in your answer.

[1 mark]

1 Read the question and read it again. What is it asking?

The question is asking you to use the information in the text to make a prediction about Grendel's actions.

2 Look for previous clues to tell you what Grendel is like.

He hates music. He is full of jealousy and hatred. He likes to eat human meat.

3 How does this make you feel?

I feel frightened and worried that something bad will happen at the Hall.

4 Ask yourself, 'What is happening at the Hall right now?'

The guards are on duty but they are asleep.

5 Link the clues together to predict what might happen next. Use evidence from the text or direct quotes to support your answer.

Grendel might kill the sleeping guards and eat them because in his song it says *Sweet human meat's the best to eat.*

6 Check your answer.

Try this

1

Matilda told such Dreadful Lies
It made one Gasp and Stretch one's Eyes;
Her Aunt attempted to Believe Matilda
The effort very nearly killed her
For once, towards the Close of Day,
Matilda, growing tired of play,
Went tiptoe to the telephone
And summoned the Immediate Aid
Of London's Noble Fire-Brigade.
Within an hour the Gallant Band
Were pouring in on every hand,
Until Matilda's Aunt succeeded
In showing them they were not needed

That Night a Fire did break out –
You should have heard Matilda Shout!
You should have heard her Scream and Bawl,
And throw the window up and call
To People passing in the Street

What might happen to Matilda in the last verse of this poem?   [1 mark]
Explain fully, referring to the text in your answer.

_____

_____

_____

Top tips

- There will be clues in the text. Go back and look for them.
- Identify how characters behave, or how events unfold.
- Do not make up information or clues and do not answer with information that is not relevant to the text.
- Refer to key elements of plot, character or information in your answer.

Understanding non-fiction

To achieve 100 you need to find information and explain how it links to the meaning of the whole text.

What you need to know

- Every piece of information given contributes to the meaning of the whole text.
- The meaning of the text is what it is telling you.
- All the texts in this chapter are non-fiction.

1 Let's practise

> Menorca is one of the Balearic Islands located in the Mediterranean Sea belonging to Spain. The name 'Menorca' actually means 'windy island'. Menorca is the first place in Spain to see sunrise each day and has over 300 sunny days every year. It has more than 100 sandy beaches and it has beautiful crystal clear waters. The island is home to around 99,000 people and they host over 1 million visitors every year.

Why do so many people visit Menorca each year?
Give **two** reasons.

[2 marks]

1	Read the question and read it again. What is it asking?	The question is asking you to say why lots of people visit Menorca.
2	Read the text again and look for something a visitor to the island would like.	It is located in the Mediterranean Sea.
3	Continue reading the whole passage to find something that would really attract so many people.	It has lots of sunny days every year, which would be nice.
4	Write this answer down.	lots of sunny days
5	Read the text again and find another reason.	There are lots of sandy beaches and clear water.
6	Choose one of your facts and write a second answer. Then, check your answers.	sandy beaches

Try this

1

> It was the best day ever! I went with my children, both boys, aged 10 and 13 and there was so much for both of them to do!
>
> We had an amazing time. My children want to go every weekend!
>
> My youngest loves animals. He adored the zoo and the petting farm. It's a must for younger children and animal lovers.
>
> My eldest and his friends love the rides. They've been time and time again. The rides are fantastic. They love it!

According to the text what makes the zoo an amazing place?
Give **two** reasons.

[2 marks]

1. _____

2. _____

2

> There is more than one way to have a successful school day, but a great way is to be well prepared. The first thing you should do is complete your homework the night before. Don't try to do your work in the morning, it will be too stressful and you may not have enough time. Next, you need to go to bed at a reasonable time. If you stay up too late, you will not be able to focus in class and you may even fall asleep. Lastly, you should wake up early. This will give you time to get ready and feel good about yourself, and you'll also be able to get something to eat before the day begins. So remember, one way to have a successful school day is to do your homework the night before, go to bed early, and wake up early. Have a great day!

Identify **two** ways the text says you can help yourself have a successful school day.

[2 marks]

1. _____

2. _____

Top tips

- Read the whole of the text again before selecting an answer.
- Once you have found one answer check that this answers the question.
- Read through the passage again to find the second answer.
- Check you have written two different answers on each line.

2 Let's practise

> *Where do we find Hiccup at the start of the film?*
> In this film there's more adventure and more challenges. Now everyone in Berk, even Hiccup's father, old Stoick, has a dragon. But Hiccup is dealing with the obligations of manhood, which are starting to pile up.
>
> *We meet some extraordinary new dragons in the film. Can you say anything about the Alpha, the creature at the top of the dragon hierarchy?*
> The Alpha is the king of all dragons and it's massive. What's cool is that instead of breathing fire like most dragons, it breathes ice and is pretty amazing.
>
> *What can you tell us about the plot and Hiccup's journey this time around?*
> Hiccup finds out that there is someone else who has the ability to control dragons. It turns out it is his mother, Valka, who he has not seen since he was a baby. He meets her, and his dad Stoick is reconnected with his long-lost love, the woman he thought was gone forever.

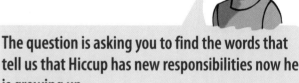

Find and **copy** the words that tell us that Hiccup has new responsibilities now he is growing up.

[1 mark]

1. Read the question and read it again. What is it asking?

The question is asking you to find the words that tell us that Hiccup has new responsibilities now he is growing up.

2. Read the text and find where he talks about Hiccup's responsibilities.

It is in the answer to the first interview question, where he talks about obligations.

3. What about the 'now he is growing up' part of the question?

That is a reference to his manhood.

4. So, what is the phrase you need to underline?

obligations of manhood

5. Remember to check that you haven't underlined any extra words.

Try this

1

When a river receives a lot of extra water it may flood. During a flood there is plenty of water, and most people wouldn't think that dehydration was a serious risk, but flood waters are mostly polluted and not safe to drink. People who drink the contaminated water may suffer from illnesses or diseases such as **typhoid**. You can prepare for flooding by filling many containers with fresh, clean drinking water. You can also use sandbags to protect your house and to soak up the water. Be prepared and be safe.

Glossary
- **typhoid** a disease that causes a fever

What does the text say is the surprising risk to humans when rivers flood? [1 mark]

Tick ✔ one.

pollution ☐

dehydration ☐

contamination ☐

flooding ☐

2

Your heart is a muscular organ, which, unlike other muscles, never gets tired.

Your heart is located a little to the left of the middle of your chest, and it's about the size of your fist. The heart muscle is special because of what it does.

The heart acts like a pump because it transports blood around your body. The blood provides your body with the oxygen and **nutrients** it needs. It also carries away waste.

Your heart is divided into four parts called chambers. The two upper chambers are called atria. They are joined to two lower chambers, called ventricles. The right side of your heart receives blood from the body and pumps it to the lungs. The left side of the heart does the exact opposite: it receives blood from the lungs and pumps it out to the body.

Glossary
- **nutrients** things that are needed for life

Find and **copy** the words that tell us what makes the heart such a special muscle. [1 mark]

Understanding fiction

To achieve 100 you need to find and explain how events are linked and contribute to the meaning of the whole text.

 What you need to know

- Everything that happens in a story contributes to the meaning of the whole text.
- The meaning of the text is what it is telling you.
- All the texts in this chapter are fiction.

Let's practise

Suddenly he – the captain, that is – began to pipe up his eternal song:

'*Fifteen men on the dead man's chest –*

Yo-ho-ho, and a bottle of rum!

Drink and the devil had done for the rest –

Yo-ho-ho, and a bottle of rum!'

At first I had supposed 'the dead man's chest' to be that identical big box of his upstairs in the front room, and the thought had been mingled in my nightmares with that of the one-legged seafaring man.

Find and **copy one** word which tells us that the captain's song scares the writer.

[1 mark]

1 Read the question and read it again. What is it asking?

The question is asking you to find and copy one word which tells us how the captain's song makes the writer feel.

2 Read the text again and look for a feeling that the writer has.

It says that he had nightmares about the dead man's chest that was in the song.

3 Remember that the question asks you to copy only one word.

nightmares

4 Check your answer.

Try this

1

> I had to do it. Just this once. Mr Adams was not going to hurt Ella any more.
>
> He'd worked his way through the class. I'd been punished more than once and I knew just how it felt. As he raised his hand, I knew I had to protect my sister. I leaped onto his arm. Mr Adams stumbled against the wooden desk and fell backwards as Ella cowered in the corner.
>
> 'Leave her alone,' I cried. 'You're a bully, you know that?' I shouted, secretly quivering inside. A noise behind me told me that the rest of the class were standing up, beating their desks with their fists and cheering.

Find and **copy one** word that tells us how the writer is actually feeling during this passage.

[1 mark]

_____

2

> **Act 1, Scene 1. A desert place**
> **Enter three witches.**
>
> **First witch**:   When shall we three meet again?
>   In thunder, lightning or in rain?
> **Second witch**: When the **hurly-burly's** done.
>   When the battle's lost and won.
> **First witch**:   Where the place?
> **Second witch**: Upon the **heath**.
> **Third witch**:   There to meet with Macbeth.
> **All**:   Fair is foul and foul is fair.
>   Hover through the fog
>   and filthy air!
> **Exit**

Glossary

- **hurly-burly** confusion/chaos
- **heath** moorland

Find and **copy** the phrase that tells us that the witches' intentions are not good.

[1 mark]

_____

Top tips

- Read the question carefully and check how many words or phrases it is asking you to copy.
- When it asks for only one word do not copy any other words.
- When it asks you to underline make sure you underline only the relevant words or phrases.
- If you are asked to underline an answer, make sure you use a ruler.

Let's practise

Sunday, 14th June 1942

I'll begin from the moment I got you, the moment I saw you lying on the table amongst my other birthday presents. (I went along when you were bought but that doesn't count.)

On Friday, 12th June, I was awake at six o'clock, which isn't surprising, since it was my birthday. But I'm not allowed to get up at that hour, so I had to control my curiosity until quarter to seven. When I couldn't wait any longer, I went to the dining-room, where Moortje (the cat) welcomed me by rubbing against my legs.

A little after seven I went to Daddy and Mummy and then to the living room to open my presents, and you were the first thing I saw, maybe one of my nicest presents. Then a bouquet of roses, some peonies and a potted plant.

Explain who 'you' is in the passage.
Why is the writer pleased by 'you'?

[2 marks]

1	Read the question and read it again. What is it asking?	The question is asking you to explain who 'you' is.
2	Read the text and find where 'you' is talked about.	It says 'the moment I got you' and 'I saw you lying on the table amongst my other birthday presents'.
3	What do you think 'you' could be?	It must be one of the presents.
4	Write your first answer down.	one of the presents
5	Now read the second question and read it again. What is it asking?	The question is asking you to say why the writer is pleased by 'you'. That means why is he pleased by this present?
6	Read the text all the way through. Can you find an answer?	It says that it was one of his nicest presents. That would make him pleased.
7	Write your answer. Then, check your answer.	It was one of his nicest presents.

Try this

1

'My wish is that everything I touch will turn to gold,' he ordered. 'I want my furniture to be gold, I want my clothes to be made of gold, I want my palace to be golden.'

The god Dionysus listened to Midas and immediately granted his wish.

The beautiful flowers in Midas' garden turned to gold when Midas approached and touched them. The king grew hungry and thin, for each time he tried to eat, he found that his meal had turned to gold. His water, his bed, his clothes, his friends, and eventually the whole palace were turned to gold.

a) What did Midas wish for? [2 marks]

_____

b) Explain why Midas' wish was actually not good for him.

_____

2

The serpent slithered slowly down, asking Eve if she would like to eat an apple from the Tree of Knowledge. 'I can only eat fruit that does not grow on the Tree of Knowledge. If we eat that, we die.'

'But you will not die,' said the serpent. 'You know you really want to eat one.

Look at how delicious it looks. It's only an apple.'

Eve gazed at the Tree and at the juicy fruit. It looked delicious and she was hungry. Surely one wouldn't hurt. Perhaps the serpent was right. She knew she shouldn't. She'd promised she wouldn't, but surely one wouldn't hurt. Eve quickly picked an apple and bit into it.

a) What did Eve eat in the text? [2 marks]

_____

b) Explain why Eve did this.

_____

_____

Identifying language choices

To achieve 100 you need to identify and comment on a writer's choice of words and phrases and how they enhance meaning.

✓ *What you need to know*

- Writers use language in different ways to keep readers interested and enhance meaning.
- Writers use imagery to create vivid images in readers' minds. One way of doing this is to use precise words (e.g. writing *willow* instead of *tree* and writing *staggered* instead of *walked*).
- Another way writers create imagery and enhance meaning is to use figurative language. This is language that has a different meaning from the literal or 'usual' meaning. Examples include simile, metaphor, alliteration, onomatopoeia and personification.

1 *Let's practise*

The reindeer were about the size of Shetland ponies and their hair was so white that even the snow hardly looked white compared with them; their branching horns were **gilded** and shone like something on fire when the sunrise caught them. Their harness was of scarlet leather and covered with bells.

🔍 Glossary
- **gilded** covered with gold

Underline the **simile** used in this text.

[1 mark]

1	Read the question and read it again. What is it asking?	The question is asking you to identify a simile in the text.
2	Similes often use the words *as* or *like* when comparing. Find an example.	The word *like* is used in the third line when describing the horns.
3	What are the horns being compared to?	They are compared to something that's on fire.
4	Underline the simile in the text.	*like something on fire*
5	Check your answer.	

46

Try this

1

> In the clearing, the piglets snuffled with no regard to the danger that was lurking nearby. They forgot to look up from the forest floor as they foraged deep into the warmth of the fetid, damp soil, rotten with decaying leaves and berries.
>
> Without warning, the weary wolf entered the clearing without making a sound. Watching from a close distance, he waited patiently. It wasn't time yet!

The writer has used **alliteration** in this text.   [1 mark]

Find and **copy one** phrase or sentence to show this.

_____

_____

2

> A rainbow is a painted smile
> turned upside down.
> It's a multi-coloured bridge
> spanning the streets of town.
>
> A rainbow is a brilliant band
> across my sister's hair.
> It's a fluorescent mountain
> Piercing the morning air.

What is the rainbow being   [1 mark]
compared to in this poem?
Write **three** things.

1. _____

2. _____

3. _____

3

> At midnight in the museum hall
> The fossils gathered for a ball
> There were no drums or saxophones,
> But just the clatter of their bones,
> A rolling, rattling, carefree circus
> Of mammoth **polkas** and **mazurkas**.

The writer uses specific sounds   [1 mark]

to describe the noise made by the

fossils. Underline **two** of them.

 Glossary
- **polka** lively folk dance
- **mazurka** a fast traditional Polish dance

Top tips

- Look for how ideas or objects are compared using words such as *like* or *as*.
- Identify ways in which ideas or objects have been given human qualities and how this helps enhance meaning.
- Identify ways in which ideas or objects with similar characteristics are compared to each other.
- Look for words where initial consonant sounds have been repeated.
- Look for words that sound like the word they refer to.
- Name the language feature in your answer if this is relevant.

2 Let's practise

Python on piccolo,
Dingo on drums,
Gannet on gee-tar,
Sits and strums.

Croc on cornet
Goes to town,

Sloth on sitar,
Upside-down.

Toad on tuba,
Sweet and strong,
Crane on clarinet,
Goat on gong.

[1 mark]

This poem contains...
Tick ✔ one.
simile. ☐ alliteration. ☐
onomatopoeia. ☐ metaphor. ☐

1 Read the question and read it again. What is it asking?

The question is asking you to identify the language feature used in the poem.

2 Read the poem and the four language choices. Remind yourself of their characteristics then look for each in turn in the text.

A simile compares one thing with another, using *like* or *as*. This is not evident in the poem, so I can eliminate that choice.

3 Are there other comparisons in the text?

No, so I can eliminate metaphor.

4 Look for alliteration in the poem.

Most lines of the poem contain two words that begin with the same sound. This is alliteration.

5 Check that there is no onomatopoeia in the poem to make sure you can eliminate that answer correctly.

There are no words that mimic the sound they refer to, so I can tick alliteration.

6 Check your answer.

Try this

1
Her face was white – not merely pale, but white like snow or paper or icing-sugar, except for her very red mouth. It was a beautiful face in other respects, but proud and cold and stern.

In this text, the writer uses a **simile** to compare ...
Tick ✔ one.

[1 mark]

a face to a mouth. ☐ a face to paper. ☐
a mouth to a colour. ☐ a mouth to icing-sugar. ☐

2

> The night is a big black cat
> The moon is her topaz eye,
> The stars are the mice she hunts at night
> In the field of the sultry sky.

In this poem, the writer uses ...   [1 mark]

Tick ✔ **two**.

simile.   ☐

alliteration.   ☐

metaphor.   ☐

personification.   ☐

3

> Round one month, oval another.
> Squashed and without air, begging to be filled again.
> White and grey marks from being kicked about and used
> on the football pitch, up in the vast expanse of space.
> The moon, just waiting to be used, waiting to make its first, victorious goal.
> Speckled sparkling spectators look on.

What is the moon being compared to?   [1 mark]

Tick ✔ **one**.

a football pitch   ☐

a spectator   ☐

an oval   ☐

a football   ☐

4

> The salmon with a hat on was conducting with a baton
> And it tried to tune the tuna fish by playing on its scales.
> The scales had all been flattened when the tuna fish was sat on
> on purpose by a porpoise and a school of killer whales.
> So the salmon with the hat on fiddled with his baton
> while the angelfish got ready to play the tambourine.

Which of the following is the main feature of this poem?   [1 mark]

Tick ✔ **one**.

onomatopoeia   ☐

personification   ☐

simile   ☐

metaphor   ☐

Explaining how language choices enhance meaning

To achieve 100 you need to explain how the language choices a writer makes enhance the meaning of a text.

✓ What you need to know

- You need to show you understand what the writer intended to do.
- Writers enhance the meaning of texts through their choice of language. Effective language choices help readers connect with texts, increase enjoyment, develop thinking skills and influence the reader's imagination and emotions.

★ Let's practise

'Where is he?' Mrs Blossom murmured, and as she spoke the clocks all faltered. Just for a second they lost their rhythm. Tick-creak-tock went the wooden clock. Tick-wheeze-tock called the **china shepherd**. Tick-swish-tock mumbled the **ormolu**.

🔍 Glossary

- **china shepherd** French clock with a painting of a shepherd
- **ormolu** a clock decorated with a gold-coloured mixture of metals

[2 marks]

What is the effect of using the words *tick-creak-tock, tick-wheeze-tock, tick-swish-tock* to describe the sounds the clocks make?

1 Read the question and read it again. What is it asking?

The question is asking you to explain the effect of the language used to describe the sounds the clocks make.

2 Why does the writer describe the sounds of the clocks?

To help the reader to *hear* what each clock sounds like – that there is something wrong with their rhythms.

3 What atmosphere do these rhythms create?

They create a mysterious atmosphere.

4 Which language feature mimics sounds?

onomatopoeia

5 Write your answer using the language feature and the purpose for using it.

The writer uses onomatopoeia to describe what the clocks sound like. The writer is trying to tell you that there is something unusual happening through the unusual sounds the clocks make.

6 Check your answer.

Try this

1

> His giant iron head, shaped like a dustbin, but as big as a bedroom, slowly turned to the right, slowly turned to the left. His iron ears turned, this way, that way. He was hearing the sea. His eyes, like headlamps, glowed white, then red, then infra-red, searching the sea. Never before had the Iron Man seen the sea.

Using evidence from the text, explain how the writer builds a picture of the Iron Man's appearance. [2 marks]

_____

_____

2

> George loves ginger nuts at school whilst playing games
> Harry's hunger never ceases especially on a plane
> Poppy picks purple plums while poking at her peas
> Jack eats juicy jelly while jigging to a beat
> Sophia slurps sloppy soup, sitting in the sand
> Betty burps borlotti beans, dancing to the band

In each line of the poem, there are words that begin with the same letter. What effect is the writer trying to create by doing this? [1 mark]

_____

_____

3

> It was a genie. No doubt about it. He was no taller than her pencil and mist still curled around him; but he looked like every genie she had ever seen in books: a little fat belly, with a silk bodice and billowing **pantaloons** that looked for all the world as if they had been woven from silver shifting mists. Tiny stars winked all over them and they were held up by a belt of pure gold. On his feet were the tiniest curly slippers, with pointed ends.

Glossary

- **pantaloons** baggy trousers fastened just above the ankle

How does the writer build a picture of what the genie looks like? Give **two** examples. [2 marks]

1. _____

2. _____

4

> CRRRAAAASSSSSSH!
> Down the cliff the Iron Man came toppling, head over heels.
> CRASH!
> CRASH!
> CRASH!
> From rock to rock, snag to snag, tumbling slowly.
> And as he crashed and crashed and crashed, his iron legs fell off.

What effect does the writer try to create by repeating the word *CRASH* in this text?

[2 marks]

_____

_____

_____

5

> 'There's a boy down the road who got some superglue on his finger without knowing it and then he put his finger to his nose.' Mr Wormwood jumped. 'What happened to him?' he spluttered. 'The finger got stuck inside his nose,' Matilda said, 'and he had to go around like that for a week. People kept saying to him, "Stop picking your nose," and he couldn't do anything about it.'
>
> 'Serve him right,' Mrs Wormwood said. 'He shouldn't have put his finger up there in the first place. It's a nasty habit. If all children had superglue put on their fingers they'd soon stop doing it.'
>
> Matilda said, 'Grown-ups do it too, Mummy. I saw you doing it yesterday in the kitchen.'

What does the word *spluttered* tell us about how Mr Wormwood felt?

[1 mark]

_____

Top tips

- Refer to an example in the text if you are asked for it.
- Describe how the language feature has an impact on the reader and enhances meaning, for example by building a better picture or changing their emotions.
- Include two or more explanations in your answer. You may achieve an additional mark for each explanation.

6

George opened his eyes and sat upright in bed. He ruffled his curly hair and in his confused state tried to make sense of the layout of his room. After a stifled yawn, it dawned on him that today was the day. The clock told him he was late. They were due to leave in fifteen minutes. George had been promised a new puppy and he was going to choose it with his dad that morning. He couldn't wait! With athletic grace, he leaped out of bed, flung back the curtains and skipped over to a pile of crumpled clothes. He couldn't get them on quick enough! As he put one leg in his trousers, George toppled over onto the bed.

How does the language of the text make you feel?   [1 mark]

Tick ✔ one.

confused ☐

sad ☐

excited ☐

jealous ☐

7

In the hamlet not a soul was visible. The buildings were like dead buildings. Their two voices rose and fell as in a dead world. The two servants, the three dogs, were without movement. Suddenly, and for no apparent reason, Irvine's servant struck a **flint** and threw, with a careless gesture, some lighted fragment on to the straw-covered floor of the **mean** barn that was just beyond the wall of the house. The flame ran along the floor and very quickly caught the bare rafters.

Glossary
- **flint** a rock used to light a fire
- **mean** broken-down

Find and **copy one** phrase that makes you feel scared.   [1 mark]

_____

Making comparisons

To achieve 100 you need to make **comparisons** in a text.

✔ *What you need to know*

- Making comparisons is about showing how information, characters or events in the text are similar or different.
- All the texts will be non-fiction.

1 ▶ *Let's practise*

They may have a fearsome reputation, but those terrifying meat-eating dinosaurs we see in the movies may have had a softer side. Some were so gentle, they were used as babysitters, according to new research. And they'd have had a big job on their hands as some trusted **juveniles** would have been in charge of dozens of babies while their parents were out looking for food. Rather than seeing the babies as a potential dinner, the older juvenile may well have been a big brother or sister helping care for its younger siblings.

🔍 Glossary

- **juvenile** young adult

 What is different about the babysitter dinosaurs compared with the other dinosaurs? Give **two** examples.

[*2 marks*]

1 Read the question and read it again. What is it asking?

The question is asking you to state two differences between the babysitter dinosaurs and other dinosaurs.

2 Locate the description of other dinosaurs throughout the text.

terrifying, meat-eating, fearsome

3 Locate the description of the babysitter dinosaurs.

softer, gentle, trusted

4 What did the parents do while the babysitters were in charge?

They were hunting for food.

5 Use the information you have gathered to compare the two types of dinosaurs. Then, check your answer.

Babysitter dinosaurs looked after the young ones. The other dinosaurs hunted for food. Babysitter dinosaurs were gentle and caring. The other dinosaurs were fearsome.

Try this

1

> Sparklers and smoke bombs are my favourite kinds of fireworks. They are both fun but they are also quite different. After you light a smoke bomb, you should put it on the ground and run. Stand back and watch it go! When you light a sparkler, however, you continue to hold it until it has finished sparkling. You wave your hand around and have a great time making patterns in the dark! They also burn differently. Sparklers create bright lights and sparks when you light them, but smoke bombs create smoke in different colours. Remember: smoke bombs and sparklers are both extremely dangerous and should only be used by professionals, or supervised by an adult.

Explain **two** ways sparklers are different to smoke bombs.   *[2 marks]*

1. _____

2. _____

2

A recent article has blamed humans for the sudden decline in UK butterflies, bees and beetles. It identified that the human population has increased rapidly: it has nearly doubled in the last 35 years. The decline in the insect population has primarily been due to the loss of their habitat because of increased human activity. As a result, the number of these creepy-crawlies has dropped by nearly 60%. You might think that this isn't a problem but actually they help us by pollinating our food crops. They are also food for other animals who might now struggle to find enough to eat.

How does the change in the number of humans on Earth compare with the change in the number of insects?   *[1 mark]*

_____

_____

Top tips

- Words to show that the text is comparing and contrasting more than one thing may include: *like, unlike, but, even though, while, however, although.*
- Questions may require you to compare one part of a text with another part of the same text.
- You will be expected to give the similarities or the differences in your answer.

2 Let's practise

Chocolate Crispy Cakes

Ingredients

75 g / 3 oz plain chocolate

150 g / 5 oz butter chopped, plus extra for greasing

100 g / 3½ oz puffed rice cereal

Method

First, you will need to grease a rectangular dish so that the cakes do not stick. Next, chop the chocolate into chunks and carefully place with the butter in a pan and melt. After that, add the puffed rice cereal to the melted mixture and stir. Finally, press the mixture firmly into the dish and chill overnight.

Chocolate Crispy Cakes

Ingredients

75 g / 3 oz plain chocolate

150 g / 5 oz butter chopped, plus extra for greasing

100 g / 3½ oz puffed rice cereal

Method

1 Grease a rectangular dish.
2 Chop the chocolate into chunks.
3 Place the chunks in a pan with butter. Melt.
4 Add puffed rice cereal to melted mixture.
5 Press the mixture firmly into dish.
6 Chill overnight.

> What is different about the way the method is written in the two texts?

[1 mark]

1 Read the question and read it again. What is it asking?

The question is asking you to compare the way in which the two methods are written.

2 How is the first method written?

It uses time connectives: *first, next, after* and *finally*.

3 How is the second method written?

It uses numbered steps.

4 Answer the question saying how the first method is different compared to the second.

The difference is that the first method is written using time connectives, and the second is written using numbered steps.

5 Check your answer.

Try this

1

a) Attention all students! Attention all kids!
Hold onto your horses! Hold onto your lids!
We have just exactly the thing that you need
whenever you've way too much homework to read.

The Marvellous Homework & Housework Machine
will always make sure that your bedroom is clean.
It loves to write book reports ten pages long,
then put all your toys away where they belong.

b) Who's been at the toothpaste?
I know some of you do it right
And you squeeze it right from the bottom
and you roll the tube up from the bottom when it gets used up don't you?

But somebody, somebody here – you know who you are,
you dig your thumb in, anywhere, anyhow,
and you've turned that tube of toothpaste into a squashed sock

Give **one** way in which the structure of the first poem is different to the
second poem.

[1 mark]

_____

_____

2

During the summer, parents are often looking for exciting places to go and
things to do to entertain their children close to home that won't cost a fortune.
Libraries are a useful resource. They often provide free book trails or challenges,
invite authors to read, and hold dressing up sessions for younger children. Local
community groups regularly provide sports and arts and craft activities at reduced
costs or for a small donation.

Looking for something interesting to do with your children this holiday? If you
are willing to look further afield, and spend a little money to keep your children
entertained, trips to the theatre, theme parks and popular museums offer endless
opportunities to distract and amuse children of all ages. Child-friendly activity
centres provide a wide range of outdoor activities from canoeing and abseiling
to archery and climbing. Children can visit on a daily basis or stay, *parent free*,
overnight! Although slightly more expensive, these mini breaks do provide the
opportunity for children to become independent and make a new set of friends.

Write **one** thing that is different about the places close to home compared
with those further afield.

[1 mark]

_____

_____

Glossary

Alliteration A series of words in which the same sound is repeated.

Antonym A word that is the opposite of another.

Comparisons Making the link between two similar things.

Context Background information to make the meaning clearer.

Empathise To put yourself in the situation of someone else.

Figurative language Words whose meaning is different from the usual meaning.

Imagery Using words to allow the reader to paint images in their imagination.

Imperative verb A verb that commands or requests (e.g. *hold*, *cook*, *push*, *write*).

Inference A conclusion reached on the basis of reasoning and evidence.

Key details Specific information that contributes to the main idea in a piece of writing.

Language features The ways in which writers communicate meaning through word choice and sentence structure.

Main idea The most important piece of information the writer wants you to know.

Metaphor When one object is described as another: *the sun is a golden apple*.

Onomatopoeia Language imitating the sound of an object or action.

Opinion A view about something, not necessarily based on fact or knowledge.

Paraphrase To reword something written or spoken using different words.

Personification Language giving human qualities to an animal or an object.

Prediction Working out what will happen next using the information you are given.

Quote To repeat or copy words from the text.

Retrieve To find something in a text (usually information).

Scan To search for specific information.

Simile A way to compare one thing to another using the words 'like' or 'as'.

Skim To read quickly to note the important points.

Summarise To give a brief statement of the main points.

Synonym A word that has the same, or very similar, meaning to another word.

Answers

Note: *Answers provided are suggestions. Always use professional judgement when considering children's responses.*

Understanding words in context (pages 9–11)

1 **1** tick: energised
  2 tick: intense
2 **1** broken up; disintegrated
  2 revellers
  3 half-forgotten, half-remembered times; made-up memories; blurred

Explaining words in context (page 13)

1 Award 2 marks for response referring to the text: It says 'tock-ticking' and an 'unwinding' of the clocks, which suggests a confusion in the mechanism of the clocks which seemed to be going backwards or slowing down / doing the opposite to the usual movements. Award 1 mark for an understanding of the phrase: They're confused because they're doing the opposite. / They're going backwards. / They're slowing down.

2 They are really tempting. / They are attractive. / You can't stop playing on them.

3 Eva liked to be noticed, she liked to 'show off and brag about her grades'.

Retrieving and recording information (pages 15–19)

1 **1** Award 1 mark each for any two of the following: warmth; shelter; in case you get into difficulties; entertain yourself; withstand harshest conditions on Earth.
  2 Award 1 mark each for habitat destruction; global warming.

2 **1** Godtfred Christiansen became head of the LEGO company.   1958
Two hundred kinds of toys were being manufactured.   1949
The company was named LEg GOdt.   1934
Toys were made for the United States.   1973
The bricks were called LEGO bricks.   1953

  2 *Harry Potter and the Order of the Phoenix* was published.   2003
The first Harry Potter book was published.   1997
J.K. Rowling was born.   1965
Harry Potter and the Deathly Hallows was released.   2007
The fourth book became the fastest-selling book in history.   2000

3 **1**

What noise does the blizzard make?	howling
What does the poem say makes music?	The moonrise
Who does the poem suggest that you should give your laughter to?	To the sick, the sad and the old.

2 marks for all three answers correct, 1 mark for two answers correct.

  2 Award 1 mark for all four correct: false, false, true, true

Identifying key details (pages 21–23)

1 **1** Award 2 marks for the following details: He brought out a box of chocolate bars every day after dinner. He added to the foil ball which suggests he continued to eat chocolate regularly.
  2 It tells you about different types of shoes needed for different sports. / It compares the uses for different sporting shoes.

2 **1** Underline any two of the following: animal or plant is usually buried under something soft; water fills the inside of the body and the soft parts rot away; the hard parts, such as the skeleton, are left behind; the sand and mud build up in layers and eventually turn to rock.
  2 Award 1 mark each for any two of the following: Ariel could fly. / Only Prospero could see him. / Ariel had magic powers.

Summarising main ideas (pages 25–27)

1 **1** tick: Jess had been waiting a long time.
  2 Plants in the forest are used as natural medicines / to cure illnesses. / Gabriela learned more about the medicinal uses of plants in the forest each time she returned.

2 Trying to survive / make a new life for himself (by building a shelter for a home and knowing what is available to eat).

Making inferences (pages 29–31)

1 **1** They were terrified that the dragons might start fighting again and they would be washed into the sea. / They were terrified in case they couldn't make it to the headland if the dragons started fighting again.
  2 Any two of the following: It has only had one owner so it's been looked after. / It hasn't travelled far (low mileage). / It is powerful (two or four horsepower). / It is equipped for fighting (sharp knives). / It looks good (red bodywork inlaid with bones).

2 **1** tick: To eat children.
  2 tick: Fertile soil is created as a result of volcanic eruptions.

Explaining inferences (page 33–35)

1 **1** Award 1 mark each for any two of the following: George had possibly returned from Scout Camp, ('George was at Scout Camp wasn't he?'). / He had made himself something to eat because the kitchen was a mess and the doughnuts were his favourite. / He was really hungry or he had friends round as there was, 'far too much food here for one person alone'.
  2 Award 3 marks for fully developed response referring to the text: 'A squirrel' because all the things or actions in the poem are about what a squirrel does, such as racing though woodland and hiding acorns. Award 2 marks for developed response: 'A squirrel' because squirrels hide acorns. Award 1 mark for undeveloped point: 'A squirrel'.

2 **1** Answers related to the importance of the subjects for technologies in the future:

Children are growing up in a world where space travel is possible so these subjects will help them. / Space-related jobs might be a normal thing when the children grow up. / Space-related jobs might replace computing jobs as we know them. / They are all subjects that might help when considering working in the fields of space research.

2 Upset / devastated / angry / deceived / cheated / lied to because: he loved the horse like a brother. Award 3 marks for fully developed response referring to the text: He was upset / devastated / angry because he would never leave the horse's side which means he loved the horse like a member of the family. / His own father sold the horse which must have made him feel worse. Award 2 marks for developed response: He was upset or angry because the horse went when he wasn't there. Award 1 mark for undeveloped point: He felt angry / upset / lied to.

Predicting (page 37)

1 The fire was real but people didn't believe her because she was always telling lies. / The fire burned down the house with Matilda in it. / The fire brigade didn't come because the people thought she was telling lies.

Understanding non-fiction (pages 39–41)

1 1 Award 1 mark each for any two of the following points: loads to do; fascinating animals; petting farm; brilliant rides.

2 Award 1 mark each for any two of the following points: be well prepared; complete your homework the night before; go to bed early (reasonable time); wake up early; get something to eat before the day begins.

2 1 tick: dehydration

2 1 mark for identifying the exact words 'never gets tired'. Also accept '(unlike other muscles) never gets tired'. Do not accept the addition of any other words or the omission of any of the words outside the brackets. Any of the words in the brackets can be omitted.

Understanding fiction (pages 43–45)

1 1 1 mark for '(secretly) quivering (inside)'. All words out of the brackets must be present exactly as written with no omission, addition or alteration of words. Words in the brackets may be present.

2 'Fair is foul' or 'foul is fair' or the whole phrase 'Fair is foul and foul is fair'.

2 1 a) He wished everything he touched would turn to gold.

b) Midas could no longer eat / grew hungry / thin.

2 a) An apple.

b) The serpent / snake persuaded / tempted her. Also accept a quotation from the text: 'you will not die' / 'you really want to eat one.' / 'Look at how delicious it looks.' / 'It's only an apple.' Do not accept reference to the idea she thought it looked delicious / she was hungry without indication that the serpent had tempted these thoughts.

Identifying language choices (pages 47–49)

1 1 *forgot to look up from the forest floor; foraged deep into the warmth of the fetid, damp soil; Without warning, the weary wolf entered. / Watching from a close distance, he waited patiently. It wasn't time yet!*

2 Any three of the following: smile; bridge; band; mountain.

3 underline: clatter; rattling

2 1 tick: a face to paper.

2 tick: metaphor. personification.

3 tick: a football

4 tick: personification

Explaining how language choices enhance meaning (pages 51–53)

1 Award 2 marks for a suitable explanation: By using similes or phrases that compare his body to other things. For example, comparing the size of his head to a dustbin and the shape or the colour of his eyes to headlamps.

2 The writer uses alliteration which makes you get tongue-tied. It makes it fun to read.

3 Award 1 mark each for any two adjectives or comparisons, such as 'no taller than her pencil', 'fat belly', 'billowing pantaloons', 'silk bodice'.

4 Award 2 marks for a response which explains both the repetition and onomatopoeia, and how by doing this the author demonstrates that it is slow motion / longer / louder. Award 1 mark for explaining the repetition / onomatopoeia or for explaining that it demonstrates how loud it is as he falls down.

5 He was surprised / shocked / found it funny.

6 tick: excited

7 not a soul was visible; buildings were like dead buildings; dead world; careless gesture; flame ran along the floor; very quickly caught the bare rafters

Making comparisons (pages 55–57)

1 1 Award 1 mark each for any two of the following: You hold a sparkler but put a smoke bomb on the ground. / Sparklers create bright light. / Smoke bombs create bright smoke.

2 Award 1 mark for reference to either of the points below. Comparisons can be implied: The number of humans has doubled. The number of insects has dropped by nearly half.

2 1 Award 1 mark for reference to any of the points below. Comparisons can be implied: The first poem is a rhyming poem. The second is non-rhyming.
The first poem is organised into rhyming couplets. The second doesn't rhyme.
The first poem is a rhyming poem. The second is a conversation poem.

2 Award 1 mark for reference to either of the points below. Comparisons can be implied: Trips close to home are cheaper. Trips further away are more expensive. (Do not accept one trip is close to home, the other is further afield.)